# WOODWORKER

Terry the termite is planning to eat his way through this entire house. Try to find a path that will lead Terry from start to finish.

FINISH

Illustrated by Gregg Valley

START

cattails

# FLOWERY FAUNA

Fauna is a Latin word for animals. Many kinds of flowers have the names of animals in them. For example, there is a horse hiding in some mint leaves. That picture is for the flower called "horsemint." There are at least twelve other animal flowers on these pages. See how many you can name. Some may be very tough, so look for clues.

Answer on page 47.

Illustrated by Judith Hunt

# LOCK MESS

Jim Nasium, the school custodian, has forgotten which key goes with which locker. Can you help him match each key to the right lock?

Answer on page 47.

# TUMBLEWORDS

Scrambled on this page are nine types of bears. Find each group of letters that look the same. Then unscramble them to find the hidden bears.

| | | | | | |
|---|---|---|---|---|---|
| B | d | Z | R | b | z | K |
| S | Y | ○ | ○ | T | L | H |
| O | k | I | T | A | A | c |
| I | L | ● | HONEY | D | ‹ | R |
| i | D | / | K | I | P | ○ |
| N | R | ↘ | P | a | ə | E |
| 7 | D | A | ◎ | ⚡ | L | A |

1 _____  5 _____

2 _____  6 _____

3 _____  7 _____

4 _____  8 _____

9 _____

Illustrated by Barbara Gray

# IT'S ALL WET

This puzzle is so soggy because it contains a lot of water. You'll make quite a splash if you use the clues to fill in the right words across and down.

## ACROSS

1. Backyard rainmaker
7. Make a speech
8. What this puzzle is about
11. Two cups of liquid
13. Uh...
15. You splash right through this
16. Ball-balancing fish-eater
18. Tool for getting water off the floor
21. Atlantic or Pacific
24. An animal's home
26. Not strong
27. "Hi!"
28. Choose this ____ that
29. Used to get water from the faucet to the pool

## DOWN

1. Bubbly cleaner
2. Abbreviation for Puerto Rico
3. What clouds send down
4. Person to avoid in game of "Tag"
5. Not old
6. You blink when water gets in this
9. Baby frogs
10. Command
12. Frozen water
14. Not you
16. Cold, fluffy ice crystals
17. A drip in the wrong place
19. Washed out, colorless
20. Single bit of falling water
22. Abbreviation for Chief Executive Officer
23. A measure of corn
25. Abbreviation for Illinois
27. Chemical symbol for water without the "2"

Answer on page 47.

Illustrated by Anni Matsick

# PUCKER'S PATH

Sheriff Pucker of Panhandle City makes daily rounds of all eight buildings on Main Street. Using the clues below, can you figure out his route today?

1. On Mondays, Wednesdays, and Fridays, the sheriff's girlfriend, Polly, works at the general store. He makes that his last stop on those days so he can visit with her longer. Otherwise, he finishes up at the school.

2. On Tuesdays and Thursdays, the bank closes early, so he goes there on the first half of his rounds.

3. Checking up on any locked-up outlaws is always the sheriff's first priority. Next he likes to see if any strangers have arrived in town, and then where they are staying.

4. On the days that Polly does not work at the general store, the sheriff starts the second half of his rounds by going there straight from the bank.

5. The blacksmith is off on Wednesdays, but the rest of the week Sheriff Pucker checks on him on the way to the livery stable.

6. Today is Tuesday.

Answer on page 47.

Illustrated by Lynn Adams

# DOT MAGIC

Connect the dots to see what an early mobile home looked like.

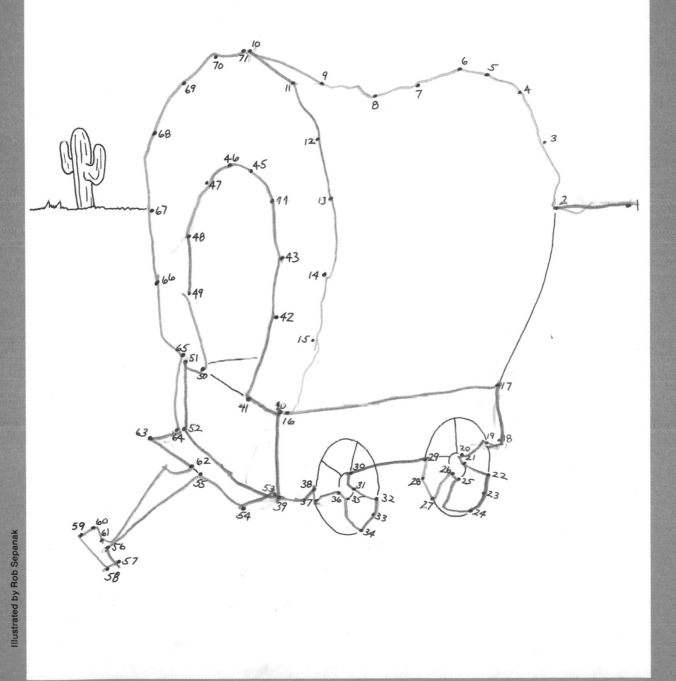

# SPACE TRACE

Captain Corey of the Intergalactic Rangers has to deliver a load of yo-yos to the kids on Grundash IV. Can you follow along the path Corey will take by matching the scenes on his view screen with the big picture before him?

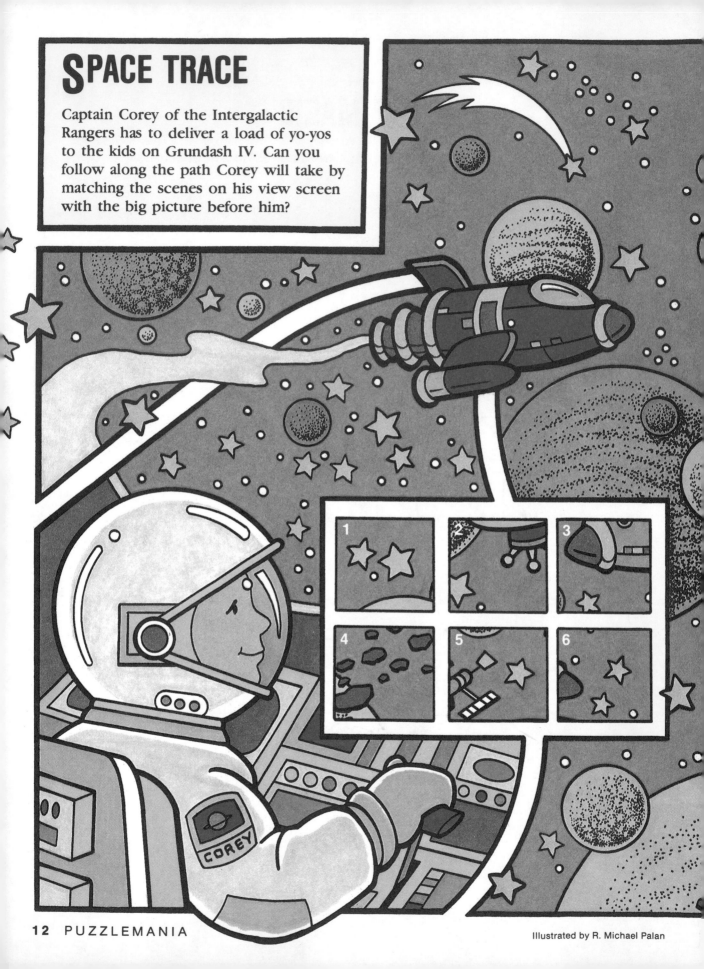

Illustrated by R. Michael Palan

GRUNDASH IV

# WHO AM I?

I was born on January 17, 1706. I was an inventor, scientist, postmaster, and diplomat. I wrote and published a famous almanac under the pen name of "Richard Sanders."

To learn my name and profession, use the clues to find seven words. Then copy each numbered letter into the answer space that has the same number below it. A few have been done to get you started.

1. A goal to strive toward: $\underset{11}{A} \underset{21}{\quad} \underset{18}{\quad}$

2. 13 plus 6: $\underset{8}{N} \underset{15}{\quad} \underset{3}{\quad} \underset{19}{\quad} \underset{26}{\quad} \underset{29}{\quad} \underset{2}{\quad} \underset{16}{\quad}$

3. A soft yellow tropical fruit: $\underset{1}{B} \underset{17}{\quad} \underset{12}{\quad} \underset{23}{\quad} \underset{24}{\quad} \underset{27}{\quad}$

4. The plaster dressing protecting a broken bone: $\underset{22}{C} \underset{32}{\quad} \underset{25}{\quad} \underset{28}{\quad}$

5. The person who tends his crops: $\underset{9}{F} \underset{5}{\quad} \underset{20}{\quad} \underset{31}{\quad} \underset{2}{\quad} \underset{10}{\quad}$

6. To squeeze into a tight position: $\underset{4}{J} \underset{23}{\quad} \underset{6}{\quad}$

7. The rings or loops that form a chain: $\underset{14}{L} \underset{7}{\quad} \underset{33}{\quad} \underset{13}{\quad} \underset{30}{\quad}$

Illustrated by Jon Davis

| B | | J | | | N | | F | | A | | | | L | | |
|---|---|---|---|---|---|---|---|---|---|---|---|---|---|---|---|
| 1 | 2 | 3 | 4 | 5 | 6 | 7 | 8 | 9 | 10 | 11 | 12 | 13 | 14 | 15 | 16 |

| | | | | | C | | | | | | | | | | | |
|---|---|---|---|---|---|---|---|---|---|---|---|---|---|---|---|---|
| 17 | 18 | 19 | 20 | 21 | 22 | 23 | 24 | 25 | 26 | 27 | 28 | 29 | 30 | 31 | 32 | 33 |

(1706-1790)

Answer on page 48.

# FOOTBALL MEMORIES

## Part 1

Take a long look at this picture. Try to remember everything you see in it. Then turn the page, and try to answer some questions about it without looking back.

Illustrated by John Nez

DON'T READ THIS UNTIL YOU HAVE LOOKED AT "Football Memories" ON PAGE 15.

# FOOTBALL MEMORIES   Part 2

Can you answer these questions about the football scene you saw? Don't peek!

1. Which team was the home team?
2. Who was winning?
3. What color were the cheerleaders' sweaters?
4. Was it a windy day?
5. What was the referee doing?
6. What number player was carrying the ball?
7. Which instrument was carried by the musician in front?
8. What quarter is it?

Answer on page 48.

# SHOW AND TELL

Can you tell which letters show up in:

1. a rectangle only?
2. both a circle and a triangle?
3. a triangle only?
4. both a square and a circle?
5. a triangle, a circle, and a rectangle?

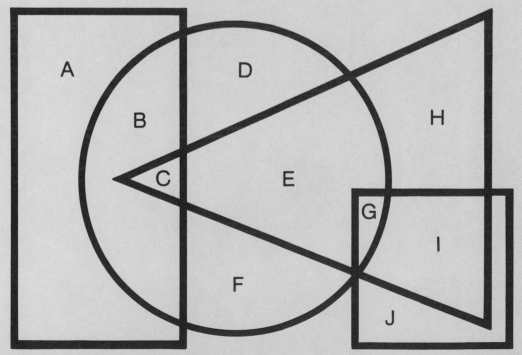

Answer on page 48.

# WHAT'S IN A WORD?

A delicious hunk of watermelon tastes great on a hot day. But did you ever notice that it's made up of two words, WATER and MELON? There are at least 40 words of three letters or more that can be made from those letters. Take a big bite and see how many words you can spit out of WATERMELON.

_____

_____

_____

_____

_____

_____

_____

_____

_____

_____

_____

_____

_____

_____

_____

Answer on page 48.

# HIDDEN PICTURES

There are at least 26 objects hidden in this picture.
How many can you find?

HOT DOGS

PRETZELS

Boddy

19

# KING OF THE BEACH

These pictures are out of order. Can you number them
to show what happened first, second, and so on?

Answer on page 48.

# HIGH-WIRE HIJINKS

The Bumbling Brothers Circus has a great new act up on the high wire. Is it a hippo in high heels? Or maybe a tiger tossing tomatoes? Quickly draw the answer before the act is over.

Illustrated by John Nez

# FULL SCALE

Do you know a ton of stuff or are you a lightweight? If you think you're a heavy hitter, step on the scale and see how many of these questions you can answer.

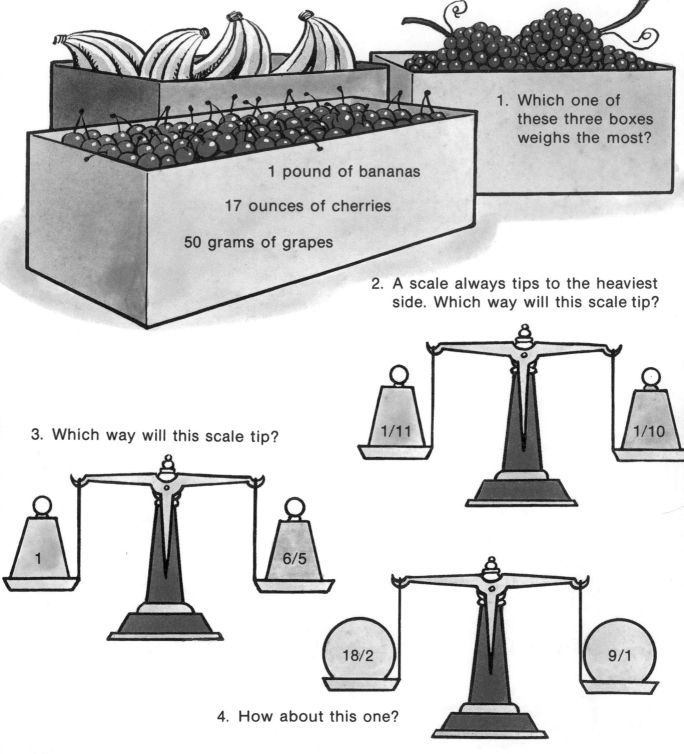

1 pound of bananas

17 ounces of cherries

50 grams of grapes

1. Which one of these three boxes weighs the most?

2. A scale always tips to the heaviest side. Which way will this scale tip?

1/11    1/10

3. Which way will this scale tip?

1    6/5

18/2    9/1

4. How about this one?

Illustrated by Terry Rogers

5. Which of these are light enough to float on water?

rock

lead

paper

glass

chocolate

wood

6. Which of these bags is the heaviest?

10 lbs. STEEL

10 lbs. FEATHERS

Answer on page 48.

# AND THE WINNER IS . . .

Rhonda and her road-running roommates just finished their first race. But they ran away with the ribbons still attached! Now no one knows who came in first, second, or third. Can you follow the ribbons to see where each runner finished?

Second

THIRD

FIRST

BETH

RHONDA

AMY

Illustrated by R. Michael Palan

Answer on page 48.

# A SPECIAL RELATIONSHIP

The words in the list below share a special relationship. The first
pair of words is set up like the second pair should be. Use them as
clues to find the words that fit in the empty spaces. When you
finish, put the starred letters in order on the lines at the bottom.
This will reveal what kind of relationship these words share.

IN is to OUT as UP is to __ __ __ __ .
                                *

STOP is to GO as FULL is to __ __ __ __ __ .
                                       *

RUN is to WALK as WORK is to __ __ __ __ .
                                *

CLEAN is to DIRTY as CAT is to __ __ __ .
                                *

BACK is to FRONT as DANGEROUS is to __ __ __ __ .
                                         *

FAST is to SLOW as NOISY is to __ __ __ __ __ .
                                     *

HOT is to COLD as SHORT is to __ __ __ __ .
                                *

TOP is to BOTTOM as PROUD is to __ __ __ __ __ __ .
                                             *

CURIOUS is to BORED as NEW is to __ __ __ __ .
                                  *

These words are all __ __ __ __ __ __ __ __ .

Illustrated by Margeaux Lucas

# THE CASE OF THE FRENZIED FROG

See if you can solve this mystery. Read the story and fill in the
missing words. Then match the numbered letters with the
matching spaces at the end of the story. If you fill in the spaces
correctly, you should be able to figure out how the frog escaped.

The June __ __ __ was shining brightly, and the sky was a
           15

clear __ __ __ __ as Croaker and Myron, two young frogs, frolicked happily
      13    3

in the green __ __ __ __ __ of the lawn. When they noticed that one of the
             5    7

__ __ __ __ __ __ __ of a nearby house was open, they leaped up to the
        11

sill and went through into a big kitchen.

In the center of the room was a __ __ __ __ __ with flowers on it and
                                 18    20

four __ __ __ __ __ __ to sit on. In the center of the table was a big deep
     10    25

bowl.

Myron, always curious, jumped to the edge of the bowl. Suddenly, he lost his

balance and __ __ __ __ into a large amount of thick cream. Since the
            16

__ __ __ __ was deep and slippery, poor Myron couldn't crawl out. He had
19

to swim round and round in that thick

__ __ __ __ __ until he was so
4

__ __ __ __ __ he could hardly move.
22    14

Meanwhile, Croaker, who could hear his friend's cries for __ __ __ __ , ran
                                                          9
off to find someone to assist him. After some time, he arrived back at the house

with Mrs. Cluck, the little red __ __ __ , Fluffy, the big tabby __ __ __ ,
                                 2                                          12
and Rover, the clever __ __ __ . Working __ __ __ __ __ __ __ __ ,
                       17                                      24
they all got through the window and approached the table. They didn't hear a

sound.

"Oh, dear," said Croaker. "We're too __ __ __ __ . Poor Myron has drowned!"
                                      7   23
"No, I haven't," said a voice, and Myron appeared from behind the bowl.

"How did you get __ __ __ ?" cried his friends.
                  1
"I kept swimming in that __ __ __ __ __ ," he answered, "until I could
                          6   8
__ __ __ __ out." And he explained how his splashing had gotten him out.
21
How did Myron's splashing help him jump out of the bowl?

__ __ __   __ __ __ __ __   __ __ __   __ __ __ __ __ __
 1  2  3    4  5  6  7  8    9 10 11   12 13 14 15 16 17
__ __   __ __ __ __ __ __ .
18 19   20 21 22 23 24 25

Answer on page 48.

# ROW, ROW, ROW

There are a lot of grandmothers out shopping for bargains. Each grandmother has something in common with the two others in the same row. For example, all the grandmothers in the top row across are wearing sunglasses. Look at the other rows across, down, and diagonally. What's the same about each row of three?

Illustrated by Barbara Gray

Answer on page 49.

# STOP, LOOK, AND LIST

Under every category, list one thing that begins with each letter. For example, one African country that begins with "M" is Mali. See if you can name another.

## African Countries

M _____

A _____

L _____

N _____

E _____

## Body Parts

M _____

A _____

L _____

N _____

E _____

## Five-Letter Words Containing A "V"

M _____

A _____

L _____

N _____

E _____

Illustrated by Lisa Dayer

Answer on page 49.

# PICTURE MIXER

Copy these mixed-up squares in the spaces on the next page to put this picture back together. The letters and numbers tell you where each square belongs. The first one, A-3, has been done for you.

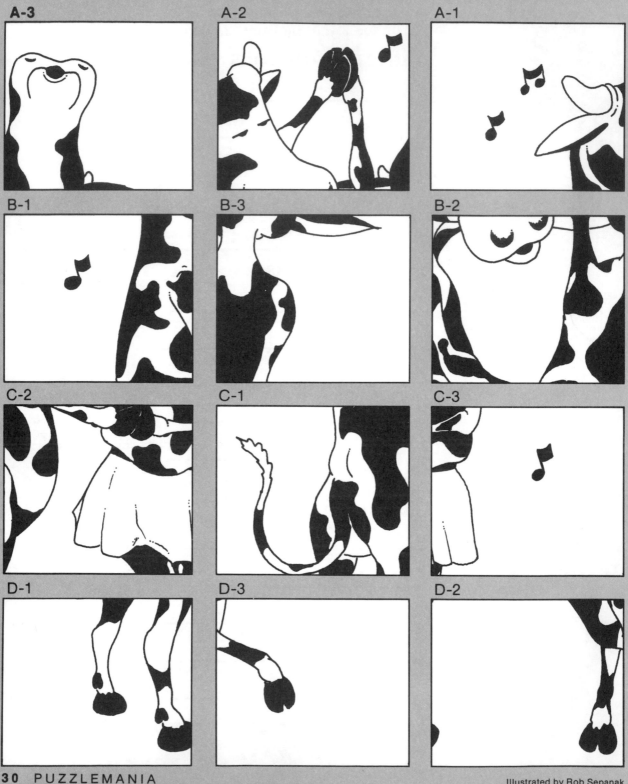

Illustrated by Rob Sepanak

|   | 1 | 2 | 3 |
|---|---|---|---|
| A |   |   |   |
| B |   |   |   |
| C |   |   |   |
| D |   |   |   |

Answer on page 49.

# BUDDY BEAR'S BIRTHDAY BASH

There are at least twelve differences between these pictures. How many can you find?

Illustrated by R. Michael Palan

# WHALE WATCH

Whales are the largest mammals on earth.
Seventeen species of whales are swimming in
the letters below. See how many you can find by
looking up, down, across, backward, and diagonally.

| | | | |
|---|---|---|---|
| | Caa'ing | Minke | Sei |
| Beaked | Fin | Narwhal | Sperm |
| Beluga | Gray | Orca | White |
| Blue | Humpback | Pilot | |
| Bowhead | Killer | Right | |

```
W           Y
  N   R     A H
    I   R A A
    G   F       B M A C M D M A
    H   L     L A H W R A N E A L S
    T   S   U O C H E E G A N K C M S
        R E L L I K H G U T I S A R W H
        M I T N W P I L O T N L E O A
        E I O I A N E H A L G P B
        M B H U M P B A C K E S
```

Illustrated by Gregg Valley

Answer on page 49.

# CALLING MR. PRESIDENT

You can call up some presidents of the United States by choosing the letters off the buttons of a telephone. The problem is that on a phone, each number, 2 through 9, can stand for three different letters. For example, the 2 might stand for A, B, or C. Your challenge is to decide which letter goes with each number in order to form the names of 19 American presidents.

1) **9 4 5 7 6 6**

2) **7 3 2 4 2 6**

3) **2 8 2 4 2 6 2 6**

4) **6 4 9 6 6**

5) **7 6 5 5**

6) **5 4 6 2 6 5 6**

7) **2 2 7 8 3 7**

8) **2 3 2 6 7**

9) **4 6 6 8 3 7**

10) **2 8 7 4**

11) **4 7 2 6 8**

12) **6 2 3 4 7 6 6**

13) **4 2 7 3 4 6 4**

14) **8 7 8 6 2 6**

15) **8 2 3 8**

16) **4 2 7 3 4 3 5 3**

17) **2 7 8 4 8 7**

18) **5 6 4 6 7 6 6**

19) **6 6 6 7 6 3**

Answer on page 49.

Illustrated by Terry Rogers

1 _____

2 _____

3 _____

4 _____

5 _____

6 _____

7 _____

8 _____

9 _____

10 _____

11 _____

12 _____

13 _____

14 _____

15 _____

16 _____

17 _____

18 _____

19 _____

# WHERE IN THE WORLD?

From these pictures, can you tell what
American cities Sarah and Sam visited last year?

1.

2.

3.

4.

5.

6.

Illustrated by Judith Hunt

Answer on page 49.

# RAP IT UP

Each of the words below contains the word RAP. Use the clues to figure out the rest of the words. Once you get the hang of it, you should wrap this up in no time.

1. ___ r a p      To cover a gift with festive paper

2. ___ r a p      A device used for catching something

3. r a p ___ ___      Moving with great speed

4. ___ r a p ___      A diagram or chart

5. ___ ___ r a p      A long, narrow strip used for securing something in place

6. ___ r a p ___ ___      A delicious ice cream drink

7. ___ ___ r a p ___      To scratch something with a sharp or rough edge

8. ___ r a p ___ ___      Green or purple berries that grow on vines

9. ___ r a p ___ ___ ___      A swinging bar used in a circus

10. ___ r a p ___ ___ ___      Vivid; very clear

Answer on page 49.

Illustrated by Jon Davis

# PENTAGON PLENTY

A pentagon is a five-sided figure that looks like this: ⬠. There are plenty of pentagons hidden in the picture below. See how many you can find.

Illustrated by Lynn Adams

# UP A TREE

While Chat R. Box, the squirrel, was out gathering food, the family started cleaning the yard. Can you help Chat find a way through all this activity so he can safely reach his cozy nest?

Illustrated by Charles Jordan

Answer on page 49.

# LAND HO!

There are many countries and regions that have the word LAND in their names, like England or Holland. Twenty-one such places fit into the squares on the next page. Use the number of letters in some names as clues to see where they go. It may help to cross each land off the list when you find its right spot. Happy landings!

**11 Letters**

Netherlands
Switzerland

**6 Letters**

Poland

**8 Letters**

Falkland      Thailand
Scotland      Togoland
Shetland      Zululand

**9 Letters**

Greenland
Sjaelland
Swaziland

**7 Letters**

England      Ireland
Finland      Lapland
Iceland

**10 Letters**

New Zealand
Somaliland

**12 Letters**
Newfoundland
Victorialand

Answer on page 50.

# SPOONERISMS

Spoonerisms are words that result when your tongue gets a little ahead of your brain and what you want to say comes out all mixed up. For example, Bonkey Mars is a spoonerism of Monkey Bars. Usually, only the first letters get switched, but sometimes it's more. See if you can figure out these other spoonerisms. It may help to say each one out loud.

FOG DOOD

CLOUNTAIN MIMING

TION LAMER

METCHUP AND CUSTARD

BEDDY TEAR

PISGETTI

KEYS AND PARROTS

BUBBERAND

GRIDE AND BROOM

SITCHEN KINK

PHELETONE

FLUTTERBYE

BITE LULB

Illustrated by Jeff Stahler

Answer on page 50.

# INSTANT PICTURE

What's hidden in these murky depths? To find out, fill in every space containing two dots.

Illustrated by Rob Sepanak

Answer on page 50.

# BEASTLY BEDS

Here are ten sleepyheads and ten cozy beds. Draw a line from each animal to the spot where you think it will go to take a nap.

Answer on page 50.

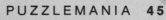

# ALL CLEAR

Clara is undercover, looking for clues. She's after words that begin with the letters CL. The way is clear, so be clever and claim as many "CL" words as you can.

Illustrated by Barbara Gray

# ANSWERS

## WOODWORKER (page 3)

## FLOWERY FAUNA (pages 4-5)
Some of the plants pictured here, from left to right, are:
1. horsemint
2. spiderflower
3. cattails
4. goatsbeard
5. snapdragon
6. white snakeroot
7. crab grass
8. skunk cabbage
9. dandelion
10. lamb's ears
11. foxglove
12. larkspur
13. hens and chickens
14. tiger lily

## LOCK MESS (page 6)
1 - A    4 - B
2 - C    5 - F
3 - E    6 - D

## TUMBLEWORDS (page 7)
KODIAK
KOALA
PANDA
TEDDY
BLACK
BROWN
POLAR
GRIZZLY
SLOTH

## IT'S ALL WET (pages 8-9)

## PUCKER'S PATH (page 10)
1. Jail               5. General store
2. Stage Depot        6. Blacksmith
3. Hotel              7. Livery stable
4. Bank               8. School

## DOT MAGIC (page 11)

## SPACE TRACE (pages 12-13)

## WHO AM I? (page 14)
1. aim
2. nineteen
3. banana
4. cast
5. farmer
6. jam
7. links

Benjamin Franklin,
American Statesman

## FOOTBALL MEMORIES (page 16)
1. The Lions
2. The Tigers, 7-0
3. Yellow
4. Yes, because the flags are moving.
5. Blowing his whistle
6. 12
7. Tuba
8. If the band is taking the field, it must be the end of the second quarter.

## SHOW AND TELL (page 16)
1. A
2. C E G
3. H
4. G
5. C

## WHAT'S IN A WORD? (page 17)
Here are the words we found. You may have found others.

| | |
|---|---|
| arm | new |
| art | now |
| ate | one |
| ear | orate |
| earn | ore |
| eat | rat |
| eel | rate |
| eon | raw |
| lane | real |
| lame | ream |
| later | real |
| law | roam |
| lean | row |
| lemon | tale |
| loan | tame |
| lone | tan |
| lore | tear |
| low | ten |
| male | ton |
| mane | tone |
| meal | tore |
| meat | torn |
| mere | tree |
| moan | want |
| moat | warm |
| mole | warn |
| more | wart |
| mow | wear |
| name | welt |
| near | wore |
| neat | won |
| net | |

## KING OF THE BEACH (page 20)
| | |
|---|---|
| 4 | 1 |
| 3 | 6 |
| 5 | 2 |

## FULL SCALE (pages 22-23)
1. A pound is only 16 ounces, while it takes 454 grams to equal one pound. So 17 ounces is the heaviest amount.
2. 1/10 is heavier than 1/11.
3. 1 is only equal to 5/5, so 6/5 is heavier.
4. Both weights equal the same amount, so the scale will stay balanced.
5. Paper and wood are the only items here that will float on water.
6. 10 pounds of anything is still only 10 pounds, so both bags weigh the same.

## AND THE WINNER IS . . . (page 24)
First - Rhonda    Second - Amy    Third - Beth

## A SPECIAL RELATIONSHIP (page 25)
Down
Empty
Play
Dog
Safe
Quiet
Tall
Humble
Used

These words are all OPPOSITES.

## THE CASE OF THE FRENZIED FROG (pages 26-27)
The June SUN was shining brightly, and the sky was a clear BLUE as Croaker and Myron, two young frogs, frolicked happily in the green GRASS of the lawn. When they noticed that one of the WINDOWS of a nearby house was open, they leaped up to the sill and went through into a big kitchen.

In the center of the room was a TABLE with flowers on it and four CHAIRS to sit on. In the center of the table was a big deep bowl.

Myron, always curious, jumped to the edge of the bowl. Suddenly, he lost his balance and FELL into a large amount of thick cream. Since the BOWL was deep and slippery, poor Myron couldn't crawl out. He had to swim round and round in that thick CREAM until he was so TIRED he could hardly move.

Meanwhile, Croaker, who could hear his friend's cries for HELP, ran off to find someone to assist him. After some time, he arrived back at the house with Mrs. Cluck, the little red HEN, Fluffy, the big tabby CAT, and Rover, the clever DOG. Working TOGETHER, they all got through the window and approached the table. They didn't hear a sound.

"Oh, dear," said Croaker. "We're too LATE. Poor Myron has drowned!"

"No, I haven't," said a voice, and Myron appeared from behind the bowl.

"How did you get OUT?" cried his friends.

"I kept swimming in that CREAM," he answered, "until I could JUMP out." And he explained how his splashing had gotten him out.

How did Myron's splashing help him jump out of the bowl?

T H E  C R E A M  H A D  T U R N E D
1 2 3  4 5 6 7 8  9 10 11  12 13 14 15 16 17
T O  B U T T E R .
18 19  20 21 22 23 24 25

## ROW, ROW, ROW (page 28)

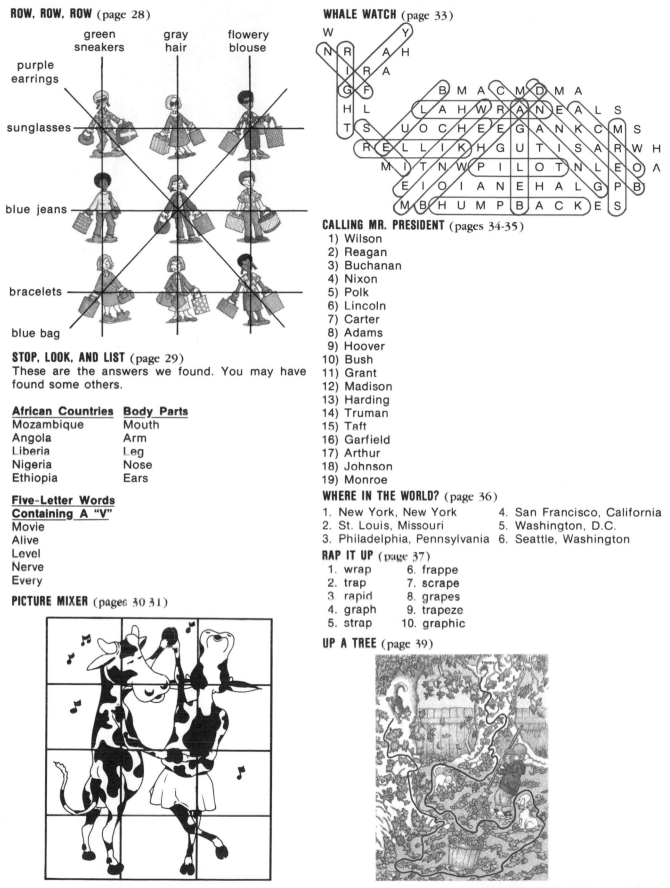

## STOP, LOOK, AND LIST (page 29)
These are the answers we found. You may have found some others.

| African Countries | Body Parts |
| --- | --- |
| Mozambique | Mouth |
| Angola | Arm |
| Liberia | Leg |
| Nigeria | Nose |
| Ethiopia | Ears |

**Five-Letter Words Containing A "V"**
Movie
Alive
Level
Nerve
Every

## PICTURE MIXER (pages 30-31)

## WHALE WATCH (page 33)

## CALLING MR. PRESIDENT (pages 34-35)
1) Wilson
2) Reagan
3) Buchanan
4) Nixon
5) Polk
6) Lincoln
7) Carter
8) Adams
9) Hoover
10) Bush
11) Grant
12) Madison
13) Harding
14) Truman
15) Taft
16) Garfield
17) Arthur
18) Johnson
19) Monroe

## WHERE IN THE WORLD? (page 36)
1. New York, New York
2. St. Louis, Missouri
3. Philadelphia, Pennsylvania
4. San Francisco, California
5. Washington, D.C.
6. Seattle, Washington

## RAP IT UP (page 37)
1. wrap
2. trap
3. rapid
4. graph
5. strap
6. frappe
7. scrape
8. grapes
9. trapeze
10. graphic

## UP A TREE (page 39)

## LAND HO! (pages 40-41)

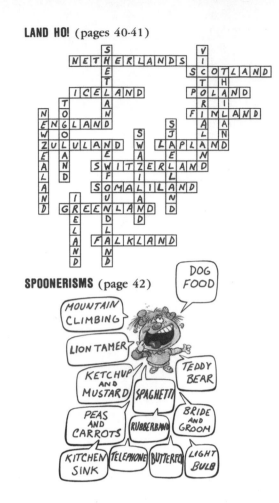

## INSTANT PICTURE (page 43)

## SPOONERISMS (page 42)

## BEASTLY BEDS (pages 44-45)